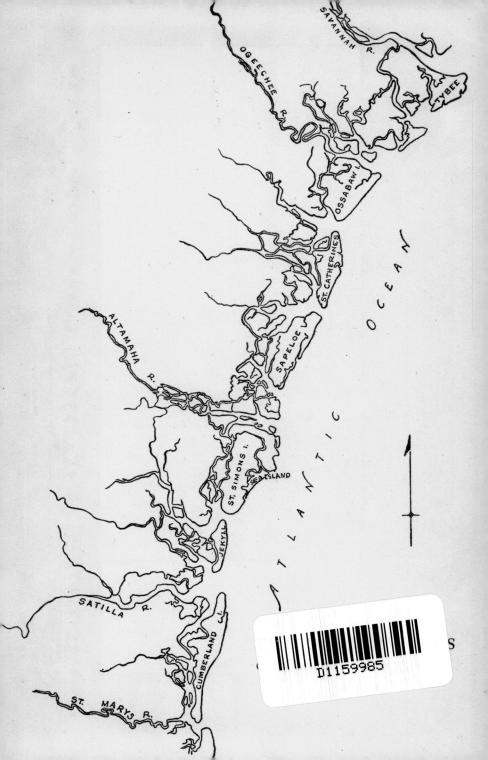

SAVANNAH R.

OGEECHEE R.

TYBEE

OSSABAW I.

ST. CATHERINES I.

ALTAMAHA R.

SAPELOE

ATLANTIC OCEAN

ST. SIMONS I.

SEA ISLAND

JEKYLL I.

SATILLA R.

CUMBERLAND I.

ST. MARYS R.

Riding a Nor'easter Comber Off Sea Island

SEA ISLANDS
OF GEORGIA

THEIR GEOLOGIC
HISTORY

by

Count D. Gibson, C. E.

DRAWINGS BY
Lucy Heinrich Haase

Athens

UNIVERSITY OF GEORGIA PRESS

TYPOGRAPHY, PRINTING, AND BINDING IN THE U. S. A. BY
KINGSPORT PRESS, INC., KINGSPORT, TENNESSEE

FOREWORD

THOSE of us who live on Georgia's islands are frequently questioned about their natural phenomena. No one objects to answering these questions so far as time and knowledge will permit, but we have long realized that the visitor would probably be better satisfied if the entire matter were unified and read at leisure. Therefore, we welcome this book, *The Sea Islands of Georgia: Their Geologic History.*

Count Gibson is qualified to prepare such a work. He is a former Professor of Geology at the Georgia School of Technology and is now retired and lives on St. Simons Island. Mr. Gibson has been familiar with St. Simons from his youth and has had a scientific interest in the islands for more than thirty years.

Many things that are simple to the scientist are difficult to the layman. Mr. Gibson was confounded in *how to say* rather than in *what to say*. He pleaded that his fellow geologists would be offended at such liberties and idealistic presentations. When he was finally prevailed upon to use a style that could be easily understood by the average reader, he produced this book which, we believe, will delight the layman.

ALFRED W. JONES

Sea Island,
Georgia

PREFACE

THE charm of Georgia's islands has inspired many books. This volume aspires to be one more in the collection. It interprets the geology of the islands and being intended for the layman primarily is written in a freedom not permitted in strictly scientific circles: most matters are treated categorically, the vocabulary is as free as possible from scientific terms, and figures are given in the nearest round terms.

For whatever public appeal the book may have, credit is due Mr. James D. Compton, President of the Sea Island Company, who read, objected and deleted so tirelessly and intelligently.

It is impossible in a preface to give thanks to all who have helped, but there are some who must not be omitted. My sincere thanks to the Honorable Garland F. Peyton, Georgia's Director of Mines, Mining and Geology, Dr. John E. Rich, legatee of Dr. N. M. Fenneman, Dr. W. W. Atwood, Dr. Wythe Cook, Dr. Otto Veach, Mr. L. H. Bailey, Dr. Charles Schuchert, Dr. Carl O. Dunbar, Ginn and Company, John Wiley and Sons, McGraw-Hill Company, The Macmillan Company, Miss Annie Postell, Mrs. Maxfield Parrish, and Mr. Foreman Stevens.

COUNT D. GIBSON

St. Simons Island,
Georgia

CONTENTS

INTRODUCTION

TIDES, artesian wells and winds interest and puzzle many visitors to Georgia's islands.

A brief review of these phenomena will help to clarify necessary references later made to them.

TIDES

Tides are the combined effect of the sun and the moon on the oceans. The law of gravitation is that two objects attract each other directly as their masses and inversely as the square of the distance between them. The sun and the moon exert a gravitational pull on the whole earth toward themselves—as does the earth on them and as they do on each other; but the oceans, being mobile and not as rigid as the rocky structure of the earth, yield to their pull in a noticeable demonstration. The oceans cover three-fourths of the earth's surface and average two and one-half miles deep.

Even though the mass of the sun is twenty-seven million times greater than the moon's mass, the sun's pull on the earth and its waters is less than one-half that of the moon's influence, since its distance from the earth is 400 times greater than the moon's distance from the earth. The influence of the moon predominates but this influence is noticeably increased or decreased when that of the sun's is added or opposed. With this in mind we can more easily explain spring tides and neap tides.

It is unfortunate that the word "spring" is used in reference to tides; it has no reference to the season of the year but to those times twice each month when the moon and the sun and the earth are in a straight line position or in syzygy as astronomers term it. The only times that the three can be in a straight line are when the moon is full or when it is new. At full moon the order is the sun, the earth and the moon; at new moon the order is the sun, the moon and the earth.

Neap tides occur twice a month also—at the waxing quarter and at the waning quarter.

"Quarter" is another unfortunate term. It has no reference to the amount of the moon's illumination but to the quarter or three-quarter points of the moon's orbit as the moon circles the earth in revolution. These quarter points are halfway between the new and full moon positions and are half moons in appearance.

There are, therefore, four critical positions of the moon in its flight around the earth and since this revolution of the moon around the earth is done every 29.5 days, each quarter of the circle represents about one week.

A typical revolution of the moon is followed through. Beginning at new moon there is a spring or a higher tide than usual; the moon waxes or increases its illuminated area until it becomes a half moon in one week; it is now neap tide at this quarter point, and the high tides are not so high nor are the low tides so low as at the new moon spring tides a week previous. The half moon continues to grow for another week until it becomes a full moon and there is then the full moon spring tide. As the moon continues its flight or revolution around the earth it begins to wane and in a week it becomes a half moon again or the last quarter, and another neap tide is on. In one more

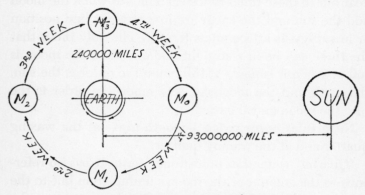

MOON PHASES AND EARTH'S TIDES

M_0	New Moon	Spring Tide
M_1	1st Quarter	Neap Tide
M_2	Full Moon	Spring Tide
M_3	3rd Quarter	Neap Tide

week it reaches its starting point of new moon and another spring tide. At the two spring tides a month the sun and moon add their influence on the waters and at the two neap tides the moon's pull is at right angles to the sun's pull; therefore, each modifies the other and together their resultant pull is smaller.

Two other equally mystifying tidal facts to island visitors are that there are two tides a day and that instead of being twelve hours apart they are 12 hours and 25 minutes apart.

These two behaviors have the same sources—the rotation of the earth on its axis every twenty-four hours and the revolution of the moon once a month.

The following explanation neglects the sun's influence for the sake of convenience in discussion. All that has

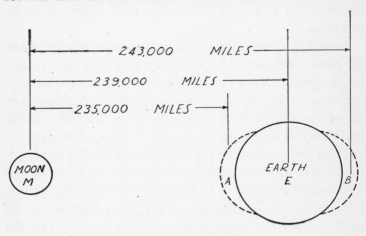

TWO TIDES DAILY

M   *Moon*
A   *High Tide Next to Moon*
B   *High Tide at Same Time as A but on Opposite Side of Earth*
E   *Earth*
Moon Draws A from E
Moon Draws E from B by Law of Gravitation

been said above still obtains, but this liberty is taken since the moon is the chief factor.

The high tide on the side of the earth next to the moon is easily understood but the high tide at the same time on the opposite side of the earth or on the side farthest from the moon gives difficulty. If it is remembered that a tide is caused by the moon's pulling the ocean waters beneath it from the earth, it is easily seen that the moon by the same force will pull the earth away from the waters on the other side of the earth and cause them to rise as a high tide there also. Ideally the waters halfway between the two high tide bulges will, of necessity, be low tides.

Now if the moon stood still instead of revolving about the earth there would be every day two high tides twelve hours apart and two low tides twelve hours apart.

However, the moon does not stand still but revolves about the earth in 29.5 days in the same direction as the earth rotates on its axis and revolves about the sun.

Therefore, when the earth makes one complete rotation it has to rotate still farther, nearly an hour, to put the moon directly over the same spot as the day before, because the moon had proceeded that distance in its orbit around the earth in twenty-four hours. Thus the high tide on the moon side of the earth is 50 minutes later each succeeding day, or, saying the same thing another way, high tides follow each other every 12 hours and 25 minutes and, of course, low tides follow each other in like intervals.

One final question is frequently asked, "Why are the tides different in height and time at different parts of the world?" To understand this one must get a picture of the ocean divided into various segments by lands or by lands and the topography of the ocean bottoms.

These segments of the fluid oceans can be likened to huge clock pendulums that have instead of weights or springs to keep them swinging, the attractive forces of the sun and the moon. By varying the length of a clock's pendulum the clock can be made to run too fast or too slow. The pendulum's length has to be regulated if the clock is to keep correct time. So it is with the tidal pendulum. If a segment of water has the proper depth and a proportionate length in which to swing in its own

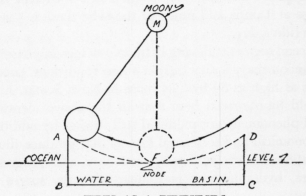

TIDES AS A PENDULUM

ABCD Is Cross Section of Basin Containing Water. Basin Tilted to Left About Fulcrum F Causes High Water at AB and Low Water at CD. Water Level at F Never Changes. F Is the Node. If Tilted to Right All Is Reversed.

natural vibration with a period of 12 hours and 25 minutes, it is in phase with the moon's impulses on the water, and tides result. But if the depth and the length of a segment of ocean water should define a natural swing differing from the period of the moon's tugs then the two periods interfere with each other and the tides of this segment would be greatly modified even to the extent of being completely nullified.

Long Island Sound illustrates a water segment such

that its free vibration periods equal its moon-forced vibration periods. Consequently the tides at the western end of the Sound have a range of 7½ feet. The Gulf of Mexico, on the other hand, is too shallow in depth in proportion to its length East and West for the water to swing or vibrate naturally in 12½ hours. Therefore, it is not in lunar phase and has very small tides. Two feet is the range at Tampa and much of the time there is just one high tide a day.

Ocean segments having harmonic swings in phase with the moon may, under certain shore conditions, produce tides as high as 50 feet, as those in Nova Scotia. And it should be observed here that all the above mentioned tidal phenomena are modified still further by additional astronomical and terrestrial factors that produce diurnal variations in range, bores, stationary and progressive waves, hydraulic and rectilinear currents, surges and seiches.

The expression "tidal wave" is frequently used. This is to be regretted since there is no such tidal action. What does occur sometimes is a seismic surge where an earthquake transmits its vibrations to the overlying sea waters. Huge waves frequently rush over bordering shores with terrifying and destructive force.

Neap tide is frequently called "Nip tide" by seafaring and coast wise folk.

Flood tide is that period when the water flows toward the land or is rising. Ebb tide is when it flows back to the sea or is falling. While ebb tides are actually of longer duration than flood tides, for practical purposes they may each be considered of six-hour durations.

ARTESIAN WELLS

Artesian wells are so named because they were first developed in Artois, France. The ancient name of Artois was Artesium.

In 1750 the French began to use the artesian well and since that time its use has spread over the earth wherever sedimentary rock layers fulfill the requirements.

A true artesian well flows freely and continuously, if unhampered, at the surface of the earth; it is a man-made spring. Requirements for such a well and certain springs are the same.

Sedimentary rocks are laid down generally in strata or layers which vary principally in kind as conglomerate, sandstone, limestone, and shale. Water passes freely through some of these rocks and with difficulty through others, according to their porosity.

If the interstitial pores are large, as in conglomerates and sandstones, they are said to be pervious. But if the pores are too small for water to move perceptibly the rock is said to be impervious, as shale and clay. Porous limestones are quite pervious.

Essential conditions for artesian wells are: a porous rock stratum which has a slope from its surface outcrop to the place of the well; the porous stratum must be confined above and below by impervious strata; and finally an ample rainfall over the area of surface outcrop of the porous stratum.

The porous stratum with these characteristics is known as an aquifer since it is water bearing. The surface outcrop of the aquifer is called the recharge zone.

Artesian basins are to be found in many countries and even on some islands that are distant from the mainland, as in the Bahamas. There is also usually more than one aquifer in formations. Rainfall over the recharge zone

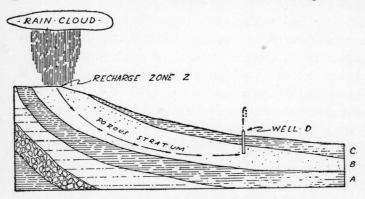

SECTION SHOWING ARTESIAN WELL ESSENTIALS
A and C Are Impervious and Confining Strata. B Is the Permeable Stratum Down Which the Water Travels From the Recharge Zone Z to Where the Flowing Well Was Bored at D.

supplies the aquifers and the aquifers do not receive waters from any other source since they are overlain by water tight or impervious layers of rocks and for the same reason they do not lose any waters except where there is a crack, weak place or a hole through which the waters escape to the surface as a spring farther down the sloping topography.

Small springs are hardly of this origin but mineral springs and some large springs are nature's artesian wells.

The force with which the water issues from wells is dependent, among other conditions, on the height of the recharge zone above the surface of the ground where the well is located. The greater the height the greater is the force. It may be said then that the recharge zone is the water tower from which run large flattened water mains, the aquifers, and the artesian wells are man's private connections to the great mains.

The rate of underground water movement varies considerably, depending chiefly on the porosity and slope of the aquifer. It ranges from one foot to one hundred feet a day usually. However, the greatest portion has a rate of less than ten feet a day.

The wells range in size from 2 inches to 30 inches in diameter and from a few feet in depth to 2,000 feet, and most all have to be cased with iron piping, at least some of the distance down.

Most artesian waters are hard since they contain lime and magnesium in solution. The odor of some artesian waters is due to the hydrogen sulfide gas they contain. If the water is allowed to stand in an open vessel a few hours the gas escapes and the taste is improved. Artesian waters are excellent for domestic purposes and need no purification treatment.

WINDS

Winds are air currents that move horizontally. Their movement is generated from unequal barometric pressures, and barometric pressures in turn depend on the fact that hot air is lighter than cold air. Since air can be heated by contact it is usually lighter over the earth's areas receiving and retaining more of the sun's heat.

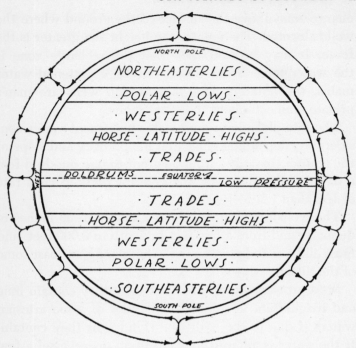

**VERTICAL PLANETARY CIRCULATION OF THE AT-
MOSPHERE**

At these heated areas the lighter air rises as vertical currents; colder air surrounding the heated areas moves in to occupy the space just vacated by the ascending air; the cold air movement is called wind.

This concept of up currents of warm air and horizontal movement of cooler air is fundamental.

The equator is the most heated area of the earth's surface. It is here that the air rises in upward currents; therefore, there is practically no wind at the equator.

This equatorial calm belt is called the doldrums. On each side of the equator the winds rush in to take the place of the ascending currents and are called the trade winds.

If the equator is the place of losing air by ascending

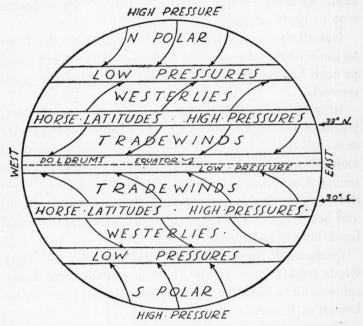

PLANETARY WINDS FOR HORIZONTAL CIRCULATION
OF ATMOSPHERE

currents and of acquiring air by trade winds, it is quite evident that somewhere on the earth there must be some descending currents in order to keep a constant supply of air for the trade winds. There is a belt of descending currents on each side of the equator—on the north it is at the 33° parallel and on the south at the 30° parallel.

These two belts are also as windless as the equator; they are called subtropical calms or horse latitudes because of a former practice of throwing horses overboard from sailing vessels when the vessels were caught in these calms for long enough periods to exhaust the drinking water supply aboard.

Not all the descending air at the horse latitudes flows to the equator as trade winds; half of it flows poleward in each hemisphere for 30°. They are called the great westerlies.

In a highly idealized description a portion of air is followed as it moves upward at the equator. It rises until it is chilled and is then moved north or south as a wind aloft. Winds aloft are usually directly opposite in direction of flow to the planetary winds on the surface. When these upper winds reach the horse latitudes they are cold and heavy enough to descend to the earth's surface and from there blow as trades or westerlies.

Because of the earth's rotation, however, planetary winds tend to turn to the right in the northern hemisphere and to the left in the southern hemisphere. This is known as Ferrel's Law.

The winds that start at the horse latitudes to blow south to the equator are by Ferrel's Law turned to the west so that they actually blow southwest from the northeast. These are known as trade winds, so called from the fact that trade is an ancient synonym of track. They have an average velocity of 15 miles an hour.

The winds that start north from the horse latitudes also turn to the right or blow toward the northeast from the southwest. Their origin gives them the name of the great westerlies. There are other planetary winds besides the trades and westerlies but these two are the most important.

Besides the planetary winds there are three other air mass movements that are important. They are cyclones, anticyclones, and the land and sea breezes.

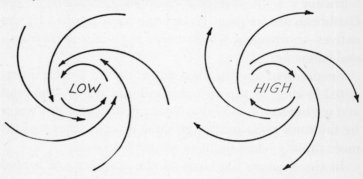

CYCLONE
Low Barometric Pressure Air Currents Are Rising at Center

ANTICYCLONE
High Barometric Pressure Currents Are Descending at Center

Cyclones are huge masses of air 500–1000 miles in diameter, which have a tendency to turn counter-clockwise and have the greatest wind velocities near the eye or center where the whirlings meet and form up-rushing currents.

The anticyclone, on the other hand, is a mass of air turning clockwise and whose currents at the center are descending instead of ascending.

When the cyclones originate north of 30° latitude they are for the most part harmless but when they form below the Tropic of Cancer they are known as tropical cyclones and some are very destructive. One more interesting feature should be mentioned in connection with these tropical cyclones. They have two sides or semicircles of varying degrees of wind force. In the Northern Hemisphere the less dangerous semicircle is on the left of the line of progression and the most dangerous semicircle is on the hurricane's right. Tropical cyclones generated in the Caribbean are frequently given the name applied by the natives—hurricanes, which means big winds in their several languages.

Finally there are the local winds caused by the differential heating of the air over land and water—the land and sea breezes. Land heats more rapidly than does water by the sun's rays, and in the same manner loses its heat more rapidly when night or winter interferes.

In the summer the lands of the seashore are heated more rapidly than the water; therefore, when the air over the land becomes heated and lighter, it flows upward and the cooler and heavier air of the sea moves in to fill the place. Thus we have sea breezes. Also from this we have cumulus and cumulo-nimbus clouds or thunderheads nearly every summer afternoon, for when the hot air rises it becomes chilled on reaching a high altitude and its moisture is condensed and often-times precipitated as rain.

Ideally, the breezes blow from the sea to the land until about one o'clock at night when the land has lost its heat by rapid radiation and the sea by comparison is now warmer since it retains its heat longer than the land. Therefore, about one or two o'clock at night the breeze starts to blow from the land to the sea and continues until about 12:00 o'clock next day. This same phenomenon of differential land and water heatings and coolings explains other local breezes on the seashore.

All differential air pressures are determined accurately by the barometer. At sea level the normal pressure is very nearly 30 inches or 760 millimeters of mercury. Even in fair weather the pressures will vary one or two tenths of an inch. But when the barometer drops below 29 inches preparations are taken against the winds that are sure to come. Slight variations occur throughout the day as mentioned and normally the higher pressures occur when the winds blow from the land to the sea.

Fogs are another phenomenon springing from differential temperatures. There are two principal divisions of fogs—air mass and frontal.

The air mass fogs are in turn divided into two subdivisions—ground and advection. Just as dew or frost is formed on a still night by radiation of heat from the ground so is ground fog formed in their stead if the air should be stirred by a very light breeze. Smoking streams on cold mornings exemplify this type of fog.

Advection fogs are caused when warm air moves over a colder ground surface. A wind blowing from the warmer sea to the land on a winter's cold night would develop an advection fog.

A frontal fog is just a cloud on the ground. Cold fronts or warm fronts alike will cause the frontal fog when conditions are favorable. Frontal fogs occur anywhere; advection fogs and ground fogs are facilitated by adjacent bodies of water. Frontal and advection fogs occur any time of the day; ground fogs begin after sundown and are dissipated by the sun next morning.

CHAPTER 1

GENERAL GEOLOGY OF GEORGIA

FROM authoritative facts alone it dawns on one that Georgia is about the most favored section of the earth's continental exposures.

Its military history under five flags is simple and rich. From its "Tobacco Road" to its Peachtree Street, from Tybee Light to Rabun Gap, from its firsts in education to its lasts in literacy, from its demagogues to its statesmen, from its intolerance to its great divines, from its lynchings to its sincere affections for its brothers in black, from its tenant farms to its outstanding industries, from the soft Elizabethan brogue of its mountains, to the equally attractive African "Geechie" of its coast, from its eroded hills to its high production of cotton, peaches, peanuts, pecans, melons and tobacco, from its grimness to its music, Georgia offers the greatest variety.

Since the history of a people is unalterably affected by the geography of their native heaths, it would be expected that Georgia has an extensive coverage of climate and geology. And such is the truth as corroborated by L. H. Bailey in his *Cyclopedia of Horticulture*: "From the rice and palmetto covered islands of the [Georgia] coast, through the vast cotton fields, peach orchards and long-leaf pine forests to the rhododendrons and white pines that cover the mountains in the northern parts, one passes through eight of the nine climatic belts represented in the United States." *

Its variety of geological features is large. Mountains, valleys, rivers, plains, swamps, lime sinks and caves, canyons, igneous dikes, earthquakes, faults, escarpments, monadnocks, springs, islands and fossils are but a partial list.

Its mineral resources include in industrial quantities water power, sands, clays, granite, marble, limestones, ochre, manganese, bauxite, barytes, iron, gold, coal and others in smaller amounts. Bartow County is one of the most highly mineralized localities anywhere.

Georgia's altitude ranges from sea level to a maximum of 4,768 feet, the top of Brasstown Bald Mountain, near the northern boundary; its rainfall varies from its minimum of 40 inches at Swainsboro to a maximum of 72 inches in the northeastern corner of its mountain section. Its extreme temperatures are from 0° in the mountains to an occasional 100°; the yearly average is 60°.

Its topographic belts are the Cumberland Plateau, the Great Valley region, the Appalachian Mountains, the Piedmont Belt, and the Coastal Plains.

Georgia has an area of 60,000 square miles and a flooded 8,000 square miles of continental shelf.

The exposed surface lies in two of the major physiographic divisions of the United States: the Appalachian region in the northwestern section and the Atlantic Plain

* L. H. Bailey, Cyclopedia of Horticulture. (New York: The Macmillan Company, 1943.)

on the southeast. The Appalachian region is divided into its mountainous topography of the northwest and the Piedmont terrain in its southeastern section. This Piedmont section of Georgia is in turn divided into plateau and plain.

The mountainous belt covers 6,000 square miles and has maximum and minimum elevations of nearly 5,000 feet in the north central to 1,000 feet on the southern border. Piedmont Georgia measures 20,000 square miles and descends from 1,000 feet on the northern line to 500 feet on the southern. The Atlantic plain has 35,000 square miles and a slope from 500 feet to sea level.

The Georgia continental shelf starts with sea level and has a negative elevation at the continental edge of 300 feet.

All these land forms have been grouped into as large units of classification as their topographic features, structures, and rock systems permit. As striking as these northeast and southwest bands of land forms are within themselves, the borders of division between them are equally as important.

There are four of these lines of separation: a fault line between the Piedmont plateau and Piedmont plain; the Fall Line between the Piedmont plain and the Atlantic plain; the coast line between the Atlantic plain and the continental shelf; the edge of the shelf terminating the shelf where the Atlantic deeps begin.

The fault zone, the median direction of the curving coast line, and the shelf edge are nearly parallel with a general bearing of N 60° E.

The median of the Fall Line's irregular curvature is

70° East of North in bearing. Columbus is its southwest terminal in Georgia. Macon, Milledgeville and Augusta are the other Georgia cities that owe their origin to this Fall Line. As the Fall Line continues beyond Georgia's borders other cities also owe their origin to it as Columbia, Richmond, Washington, Philadelphia.

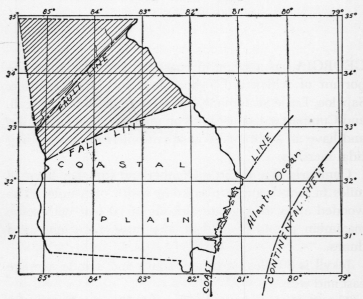

PRINCIPAL GEOLOGICAL DIVISION LINES OF GEORGIA

The coast line is the marine boundary of Camden, Glynn, McIntosh, Liberty, Bryan and Chatham Counties, and is 100 miles long. The basal structure of the coastal plains and the continental shelf is a unit set off by the Fall Line and the edge of the continental shelf. The distance between these two lines is 280 miles.

CHAPTER 2

GENERAL GEOLOGY OF GEORGIA'S
SEA ISLANDS

GEORGIA has a string of coastal islands, the most important of which are Tybee, Ossabaw, St. Catherine, Sapeloe, Little St. Simons, Sea Island, St. Simons, Jekyll, and Cumberland. They total an area of 600 square miles and have an additional 550 square miles of surrounding tidal marshes.

Cumberland and Little Cumberland together have 18 miles in length and a maximum width of 3 miles. The wooded areas average an altitude of 20 feet with some maximum points of 50 feet, the tops of ancient sand dunes.

Jekyll is 8 miles north and south and 1 mile average east and west.

The St. Simons–Sea Island unit is 13 miles long and 4 miles wide and has an altitude above mean sea level of 14 feet. Its dunes are low-lying, having a maximum height of 25 feet. St. Simons is less than 1.1 mile from Jekyll at their closest points across St. Simons Sound.

Sapeloe and Blackbeard are taken together in dimensions which are 11 miles by 3 miles. St. Catherine and Ossabaw each have about the same dimensions, 10 miles by 2 miles.

The most complex group of them all is composed of Warsaw, Skidaway, Isle of Hope, Whitemarsh, Wilmington, and Tybee.

Wolf and Egg Islands are little more than high marshes, the greater portions of which are frequently covered by high tides.

Taken as a whole Georgia's islands follow a pattern of sandy beaches on the east or ocean side and extensive salt water marshes between the islands and the mainland. The marshes are flooded and drained by salt water gutters, creeks, and rivers.

The island highlands are covered with pines, live oaks, cedars, magnolias, the cabbage palmetto, scrub palmetto, cassina berries, myrtles, grapevines, brambles, and several other trees and plants in smaller quantities. Spanish moss, which hangs abundantly from the trees, is not a parasite but an epiphyte—or air plant; and it will live on a telephone wire as easily as on a tree. Consequently it does not kill trees.

All of the islands produce small game, but turkey, deer, and bear have been nearly depleted from the more populated ones.

With the exception of hotel and pleasure establishments, organized industry is at a minimum. Commercial fishing and local farming are done on a small scale and chiefly for local consumption.

Sea Island, St. Simons, and Tybee are all connected to the mainland by motor causeways and bridges.

The geological origin of these islands is fairly simple, yet complex enough to be interesting. Some quotations from authorities are given:

Otto Veach wrote in "Geology of the Coastal Plain of Georgia," "Due to recent submergence the coast line is irregular and a network of sea islands, tidal rivers, sounds, estuaries and marshes have been formed." [*]

"The northeast storms set up a shore current which carries more or less sand and gravel southward. Southeast storms tend to develop littoral currents that move northward and carry sand and gravel with them along the shore. These alternating currents build sand bars which in time develop into sand reefs. . . . Through the salt marshes which intervene between the sand reefs and the mainland there is a network of channels. . . ." [**]

From these quotations there appear at least two different theories of the origin of Georgia's islands. They are more complementary than divergent, however, as will be shown.

The islands themselves are young and simple geologically. But the forces leading to their creation are old and complex.

Their first ancestor about which very many data have been verified is a land mass called "Appalachia" by geologists. Strangely enough the ancient Appalachia was itself an island. It extended from the Gulf of Mexico to Maryland and from the present Appalachian mountain chain on the west to include the present submerged continental edge on the East. It must not in any way be confused with the present Appalachian mountains, which were at that time in a foetal stage only and their present site was

[*] *Georgia Geological Survey, Bulletin 26 (1911), p. 26.*
[**] *W. W. Atwood, Physiographic Provinces of North America (Boston: Ginn and Company, 1940), p. 54.*

the bottom of a huge continental trough, a geosyncline, filled with sea waters and being ever loaded with eroded materials from the adjacent land masses on the West as well as from Appalachia itself on the East. The beginning

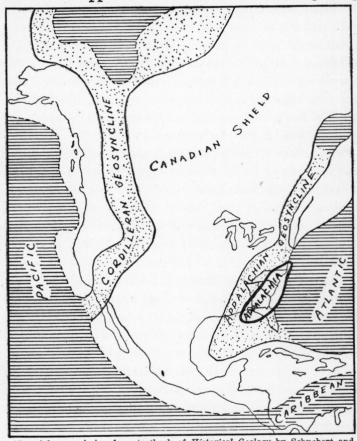

Altered by permission from textbook of *Historical Geology* by Schuchert and Dunbar, published by John Wiley & Sons, Inc.

PRE-CAMBRIAN MAP OF NORTH AMERICA SHOWING
THE ISLAND OF APPALACHIA

of the island Appalachia was probably Pre-Cambrian or certainly over 500 millions of years ago.

It remained an island for 200 millions of years constantly elongating itself on the north end until in the late Devonian Period it became permanently attached at its north end to the continent. It was now a peninsula, and remained one for the rest of the Paleozoic Era, some 100 million of years, at which time it lost this identity by becoming consolidated with the continent and at the same time the Appalachian geosyncline was inverted and the Appalachian mountain ranges were born. All insular aspects of ancient Appalachia were lost.

Even though Appalachia was now a part of the continent its shore line remained in its original position along the edge of the continental shelf for 50 million years, when sometime in the Jurassic the site of the present Georgia was invaded by the Atlantic Ocean. The ocean reached to the Fall Line and continued there for a short geological time, about 30 million years, when it again receded to its old boundary at the edge of the shelf. This return was marked by the birth of the Rocky Mountain system out of a huge geosyncline reaching from Alaska to Mexico. This was the close of the Cretaceous Period and the Mesozoic Era.

There was in the early Cenozoic, the Eocene, a return of the coast line from the continental edge back to its former Cretaceous boundary along the Fall Line where it stayed for another 50 million years and after which it retreated to within 100 miles of its present location. By periodic steps covering the last 10 million years the coast line of today was established.

CHAPTER 3

BIRTH OF GEORGIA'S SEA ISLANDS

IN GENERAL sea islands are formed under and by five geologic dynamics—diastrophism, vulcanism, gradation, glaciation, organisms or any combination of these.

Diastrophism is the crustal movements of the earth. These movements are caused by mass adjustments such as faulting, folding, continental migration. The sinking of an eroded seashore made Britain an island and a rising of the ocean floor produced Cuba.

Hawaii is an instance of vulcanism. It is the tops of volcanic ejecta piled in the sea.

Gradation includes both erosion and the deposition of eroded materials. Deltas are islands illustrating deposition.

Atolls, due to the requirements for coral growth, combine vulcanism, organisms, and glaciation. Glaciation has its greatest effect by locking earth's waters into the polar ice caps and in turn releasing these waters when the caps melt. This alternate freezing and thawing of earth's waters can produce as much as 400 feet change in ocean levels. In comparison with larger figures in other geologic phenomena, 400 feet does not seem to be so much; but one should stop to consider what effect the rise of 100 feet in sea levels would have on the cities, industries and peoples of the United States alone.

Georgia's islands are formed by at least three of the above agents: gradation, diastrophism, and glaciation. Certainly the history of Appalachia, as brought down to the Pleistocene, was chiefly under the influence of gradation and diastrophism.

Before proceeding with the recounting of the actual birth of the Georgia coastal islands a discussion of the mentioned lines of geologic demarcation is needed.

The most northerly of these lines is an ancient low angle or thrust fault zone which begins in Heard County on the western border of the State, and runs with a bearing of 56° east of north and following fairly closely to the narrow valley of the Chattahoochee River a few miles north of Atlanta and proceeding up stream through Hall County on to Rabun's Gap. This is a highly mineralized belt and is one of Georgia's gold vein areas. It is a line of structural weakness and can be likened to a huge hinge with the area below it and extending to the edge of the continental shelf acting as the leaf of a mammoth drop leaf table. In the early history of Appalachia high mountains stood over the area of Atlanta. This range of mountains extending NE and SW across the ancient island is called "Ocoee." Their height is estimated to have been as much as 3 miles. Enormous erosion continuing for 350 million years moved much of this high land mass from the Atlanta area as well as much of the overlying rocks that formed the eastern flank of Appalachia. This shifting of overlying burden of great mass plus the internal upswelling of Stone Mountain and other similar magmatic rocks of the area caused the table leaf, now a peneplain, to tilt southeastward in the Jurassic and the Atlantic sent its rolling waves, unleashed for the first time on inland Appalachia, dashing on a shore near the present Fall Line. A thirty million year period of mass erosion continued and the eroded material was dumped on the former peneplain, now the floor of the sea that had invaded this much of Appalachia.

There followed an upward swing of the Appalachia table leaf and once more the waters were forced back to their former place at the edge of the abyss. This rise of the leaf was probably isostatic. Isostacy is the principle of load adjustment. Appalachia was a geosegment of light granitic rocks forced above sea level by the lower lying and heavier basaltic rock at the bottom of the sea. But when the lighter rocks were planed off by former erosion and dumped on the heavier basaltic rocks in the abyss, a slow upward movement of the leaf took place with the hinge of the old fault zone yielding to the movement. Another structural disturbance explains the next lowering of the leaf to the extent that waters recaptured their former beach head at the Fall Line.

Isostacy became operative again and lifted the Appalachia table leaf high enough to force the ocean back some 100 miles and down some 200 feet.

From these records then it appears that the Fall Line zone is the bi-planar intersection of two peneplains, the oldest being the section from the Fall Line to the continental edge and on which have been deposited material from the continued erosion of its exposed subaerial portion. This erosion of the subaerial portion produced the Piedmont Plain and plateau, a later peneplain with a

differing seaward slope. To one traveling across the Fall
Line in an automobile it is scarcely noticeable, but to one
in a boat the rapids in the rivers make it quite apparent.
The geologist recognizes it by the abrupt change from
crystalline rocks above to the sudden appearance of sedimentary below it.

These sedimentary beds from the Fall Line to the coast
line form the coastal plain—Georgia's largest geologic
division. As has been stated these beds were deposited
on an ancient and tilted peneplain. The old peneplain
has a slope to the sea of 25 feet to the mile. This is com-
puted from oil well logs where the drilling went clear
through the sedimentary rocks and into the basal complex of the old peneplain surface. The overlying beds at
the coast have a depth of 5000 feet and 7000 feet at the
shelf's edge.

The topographical gradient of the coastal plain is 2
feet per mile and the surface of the deposits on the shelf,
or the ocean's floor, slopes at twice this rate or four feet
per mile. These beds and their tilt toward the sea account
for artesian wells. Rainwaters enter the layers of porous
rock in the recharge zone which extends from the Fall
Line for 150 miles toward the shore line.

Typical aquifers, or water bearing strata, are Eocene
and Oligocene limestones whose outcrops spread from
5 to 40 miles below the Fall Line. They have an overlying and confining stratum of impervious marl and clay
which is of the Miocene age. These Oligocene aquifers
are 400 feet below the surface at the coast line and produce wells of 15 feet flow under present conditions.
There are at least three zone depths on St. Simons from
which well flows may be obtained. It takes underground

water from one hundred to three hundred years to travel from the recharge zone to the Georgia coast.

The third line is the coast line. It is difficult to discuss Georgia's 100-mile section of the coast line without con-

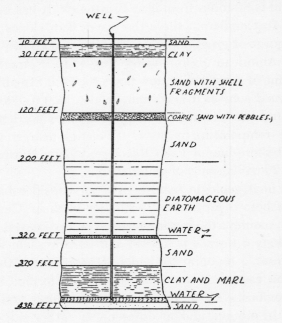

WELL

10 FEET	SAND
30 FEET	CLAY
	SAND WITH SHELL FRAGMENTS
120 FEET	COARSE SAND WITH PEBBLES
	SAND
200 FEET	
	DIATOMACEOUS EARTH
320 FEET	WATER
	SAND
370 FEET	
	CLAY AND MARL
	WATER
438 FEET	SAND

LOG SECTION OF ARTESIAN WELL
ST. SIMONS ISLAND, GEORGIA
6 Inch Diameter
250 Gallons Per Minute

sidering its continuation into Florida on the south and the Carolinas on the north. If Cape Fear, N. C., Brunswick, Georgia, and Palm Beach, Florida, are considered in geometric relation they form the arc of a circle with Brunswick at the mid point of the arc. The circle has a one minute degree of curvature. The chord of this arc drawn from Cape Fear to Palm Beach is 500 miles and is distant from Brunswick at its nearest point 150 miles.

The last of the four lines is the edge of the continental shelf which follows roughly the coast line in configuration and is 80 miles from it at Brunswick. It has a depth of 300 feet and from there the ocean floor slopes into a steep gorge of great depths, 5000 feet, and known as the North American Basin. Along this edge, formerly the coast line of Appalachia, now flows the Gulf Stream in its northward course. It is 50 miles wide, 3000 to 5000 feet deep, and has a current velocity of 3 miles per hour. Its surface temperature is 80° F. It comes nearest to the present shore line at Palm Beach and Cape Hatteras. It moves 20 trillion tons of water daily.

One final geologic feature calls for considerable discussion before proceeding with the birth of Georgia's islands, namely: the marine terraces of the coastal plain. In geology a terrace is a level and narrow plain with a steep front, a topographic bench. It may border the sea, as in this case, or rivers or lakes, and was formed by being previously an area under the levelling action of waters in motion, and in different, or rather successive stages. There are five of these terraces in Georgia's coastal plain extending 100 miles inland and parallel to the coastline. They cover the lower half of the coastal plain. Their names, altitudes and widths are:

Terrace	Altitude	Width
Hazlehurst	250 feet	20 miles
Claxton	200 feet	20 miles
Okefenokee	150 feet	20 miles
Penholoway	100 feet	20 miles
Satilla	50 feet	20 miles

These widths were measured along the highway to Macon and only ideally represent true dimensions. The escarpment at the upper border of the Satilla terrace is easily discernible near Everett City or Nahunta as one travels these highways.

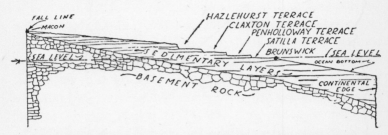

EXAGGERATED VERTICAL SECTION SHOWING TERRACES

Up to the Pleistocene one million years ago the swinging of Appalachia's table leaf, called by geologists monoclinal warping, explains the encroachment and the retreat of the seas over Georgia. But now another factor in sea level differentials takes over.

The records of the monoclinal movement of the coastal plain indicate even the shortest period to be 30 million years. The maximum displacement for that span of time was 6000 feet or an annual rate of 1/5000 of a foot and apparently at a uniform rate over the 30 millions of years.

The terraces do not indicate *gradual* emergence, but *sudden* withdrawals of wave action from the old coast lines or terrace escarpments.

In the beginning of the Pleistocene epoch there began a rhythmic and alternate freezing and thawing of the earth's waters. It takes a prodigious imagination to visualize the proportions of the glacial phenomenon of the

Pleistocene. One-sixth of the earth's exposed lands and one-half of the North American continent were covered and in some places as much as 8000 feet deep in ice. The evidence of these data is irrefutable.

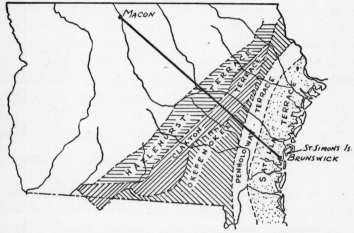

MAP OF THE COASTAL TERRACES OF GEORGIA

Further study is likely to prove that even larger volumes of the world's waters were temporarily locked in the glacial refrigerators. It is admitted by conservative glaciologists that the sea level was lowered at that time as much as 300 feet, and as will appear further on in this discussion it was probably as much as 400 feet. After each freezing period there followed a thawing, one that lasted much longer in comparison. The thawing spans are known as interglacial. Each thawing period of the Pleistocene restored less water than its predecessor to the sea level before another freezing lowered the seas again. In other words, the earth has not been free from large polar caps since the beginning of the Pleistocene.

If the polar caps should be completely melted the water level would again reach the old shore line at the top of the Hazlehurst terrace, which has an altitude of 250 feet.

It is the opinion of H. A. Marmer, Assistant Chief of the Division of Tides and Currents of the Coast and Geodetic Survey, that a rise of Atlantic waters began in 1920 from glacial melting and by careful observations is calculated to be 1½ feet a century. Today is witnessing a release of waters previously frozen. The trend may change at any time.

The rhythmic progression of terraces and glacial occurrences is shown.

Glacial Ages	Terraces
1. Nebraskan Ice Age	Hazlehurst
Aftonian Interglacial Stage	
2. Kansas Ice Age	Claxton
Yarmouth Interglacial Stage	
3. Illinoian Ice Age	Okefenokee
Sagamon Interglacial Stage	
4. Iowan Ice Age	Penholoway
Peorian Interglacial Stage	
5. Wisconsin Ice Age	Satilla

It is generally agreed that 25,000 years have elapsed since the Wisconsin freeze.

The glacial coverage of continental areas today is nothing like it was in the Nebraskan Stage and if the present polar caps would furnish enough waters from their melting to restore the sea level to the abandoned shore line of the Hazlehurst terrace an altitude of 250 feet, the volume of frozen waters during the Nebraskan must have reduced the sea level at least 400 feet.

The Wisconsin freeze and its subsequent thawings were certainly the immediate cause of the birth of Geor-

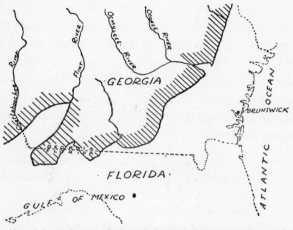

Altered from *Georgia Geological Survey*, Bulletin 42, Plate X-B.

GEORGIA COAST DURING OKEFENOKEE TER-
RACE BUILDING

gia's sea islands. But the manner of the birth is an argued question as seen from the quotations of two authorities.

Wythe Cook in "Georgia Geological Bulletin No. 42," wrote: [*]

"The next emergence about 60 feet, brought the sea level to its present position and laid bare the Satilla terrace. The shore line, resulting from this latest emergence, was very irregular because of the many low delta-like

[*] *Georgia Geological Survey, Bulletin 42 (1925), p. 33.*

banks or shoals that had ribbed the sea floor during the preceding epoch. Under the combined action of waves, winds and currents, a series of sand bars began to form off shore, rapidly grew into islands, and formed a new, straighter shore line. The little bays that indented the old shore line and the lagoons back of the islands, shut off from the force of the waves, immediately began to fill with silt. Mud and sand brought down by the streams or stirred up from the bottom by storms settled in the quiet water of the bays and lagoons. As soon as the water grew shallow enough for grasses to take root, vegetation converted the tidal flats into marshes and furthered the accumulation of silt.

"Tidal movement became restricted to definite channels which the great volume of water, rushing in or out four times each day, kept clear of sediment and scoured to depths of more than 20 feet. Intricate and complete drainage systems for each little sub area of marsh became established. Thus were formed the Sea Islands of Glynn."

N. M. Fenneman in *Physiography of Eastern United States* * says: "With the first Pleistocene submergence this partly dissected surface was planed by waves and veneered with new sediment as far inland as the sandhill belt in central North Carolina, and about half as far in Georgia. The land then rose intermittently (with intervening subsidence) a total of more than 200 feet in five acts, each rise laying bare a new terrace. While such an oscillating movement has not been demonstrated for all

* N. M. Fenneman, *Physiography of Eastern United States.* (New York: McGraw-Hill Book Company, 1938), p. 46.

of the terraces, it is obvious that the last or Pamlico terrace, after slight erosion, was again depressed to make the sea islands."

Each of these theories recounts only parts of the processes in the formation of the islands. When taken together they come more nearly to representing the complete truth as indicated by field data.

Some of the data are clay and limestone deposits in the marshes, limestone and sandstone on the islands, hammocks or islands in the marshes. Probably the most striking data are the stumps of cypress trees occupying the very positions where they once grew. These ancient stumps can be seen only at a spring tide when there is a west wind blowing. They are in the bottoms of marsh creeks and eight feet below the marsh level.

From this it is seen that at least some of the present marshes are the sites of former fresh water swamps.

Another observation of importance is the fact that each island of the chain is very similar in shape to all the rest. They have in common their axes of elongation parallel to the mainland and also have straight line contacts between the marshes and the islands on both their seaward and westward sides. It is significant that some have these marshes on their seaward sides.

Probably the best way to demonstrate what did happen to set the pattern of the shape for the islands is to check into what would happen if the ocean level should rise ten or fifteen feet on the present mainland topography. It is obvious that closed contours of 20 and 30 feet, shown on U. S. Geological Quadrangles, Kingsland and Everett City, would become sea islands with their longer axes running north and south, and the adjoining swamps, such as Hermitage and Pine Barren in Camden, and the two Buffalos in Glynn, becoming marshes.

However, these examples would not explain why all the islands have the common characteristics as listed. An explanation is quite important. In the very flat topography of the coast the drainage into rivers, sounds, and inlets is perpendicular to them; also this flat topography is old age drainage topography (age in drainage has no reference to length of existence but to the ratio of work to be done to the work already done), and consequently all its streams meander.

One of the laws of meandering streams is that their borders of lateral planation are roughly parallel to the median of their meanderings. Therefore, following the principles of this law the marshes, which are but flood plains of meandering tidal streams, have straight sides contiguous to the islands and mainland, and perpendicular to the fresh water rivers.

Resuming the discussion of the other field data, it is to be noted that the clay clumps and limestone deposits appear in scattered spots only. They are definitely older formations than the muds and sands surrounding them. The clay clumps are probably the remains of former limestone deposits that have been dissolved. The limestone itself is probably a precipitate in origin. Marsh islands such as Creighton and Little Sapeloe in McIntosh County are remnants of high spots not yet reduced to marsh by the meandering of the neighboring streams.

On the other hand the sandstone is general on St. Simons and in some areas on the mainland, so much so that it could be called a Satilla sandstone.

The particles of its quartz aggregate are grains having size and appearance similar to the present beach sands. The deposit is not thick, a few feet at most, and is only slightly hardened or indurated as a geologist would describe it. Oglethorpe's engineer, John Thomas, described it as far back as 1740 in the following quotation:

"N B It is observed all over the island where they have dug that three or four feet deep or generally about the level of high water the ground is so hard that it must be cut with a pick ax, and may be got up in great stones with care, and is the same matter as the rocks on the Sea Beach, which stone holds very well in walls of fortifications when it is plastered."

When all the field data are compared and consolidated they describe the following steps. The clay and limestone are the oldest and were formed during an older and greater submergence than the small one in which the sandstone was deposited. This small submergence progressed beyond the sandstone deposition enough to lay down the present overburden on the sandstone. Then followed an emergence, very small but sufficient to drain off the salt waters and form fresh water swamps where the cypress trees grew. Then came the last and also quite small rise in the sea level and it overflowed the fresh water swamps, reconverting them into marshes and creating Georgia's existing islands.

CONCLUSIONS

Georgia's islands had an island for an ancestor. This ancestor, Appalachia, is one of the oldest geological areas in North America. The islands and coast line are the top stratum of five thousand feet of sedimentary rock stacked in layers on the remains of Appalachia.

There were islands like them before the present chain was born. Salt marshes on the seaward side of the islands once connected some former islands with the present chain when it, the present chain, was part of the mainland.

The islands owe their immediate birth to the fluctuations of continental glaciers. As islands they were separated from the mainland one thousand years ago.

CHAPTER 4

MODIFICATIONS OF GEORGIA'S
SEA ISLANDS

BIRTH in geological formations, as in organic life, certainly does not mean a stasis in existence but a ceaseless change.

Georgia's sea islands have been subject to modification the moment the smallest section was surrounded by water. The geologist calls this change or modification growth regardless of whether it is an increase or decrease in size. Today is just one period in their growth. Their future is unalterably determined by natural forces now operative and by some that are dormant or prevented for the time being. Growth is affected not by any single force but by a combination of many.

The forces considered important are *vulcanism, earthquakes, diastrophism, glaciation,* and *gradation* by rivers, winds, waves, and tides. Some of these can be disposed of shortly. There is a slight record of volcanic ashes in Georgia's coastal plain deposits, but at present there is no indication that the islands will ever experience appreciable vulcanism.

The greatest seismic tremors, of which there is a local record, occurred from the Charleston quake in 1886.

There was no surge of rising waters. Inhabitants now living, and who remember the quake, say that the vibrations did some small damage to tabby buildings. There will be quakes in the future but none will be important in modifying the islands geologically.

Diastrophism will take its toll without a doubt. It is working now—but so slowly that it is beyond direct detection.

Glaciation has already been discussed. If it alone is considered and if there is no change in its present trend, the islands will be completely submerged in one thousand years.

The most active force, gradation by rivers, winds, waves, currents, and tides, is affecting their growth surely, visibly and rapidly in the geologist's definition of rapidly.

This group of agencies works all the time but there are special occasions when they are spectacularly more effective, particularly during storms and hurricanes.

The area around St. Simons is peculiarly protected from destructive hurricanes. Even though the hurricanes are greatly modified they cause the maximum quick changes on the islands. Northeasters are common and, while they are not the prevailing winds of the locality, according to the aerologist, they are next to the hurricane in effecting marine gradation.

The explanation of St. Simons' relative freedom from hurricanes is closely connected with the Gulf Stream.

It was mentioned that Brunswick was the mid-point of an arc. This arc can be lengthened on each end—to Miami on the South and Hatteras on the North. The Gulf

Stream itself follows somewhat the concavity of the shore line. It is closest to land at Palm Beach and Cape Hatteras, and farthest from the shore at a point opposite St. Simons, a distance of 80 miles.

The hurricanes breed in the Caribbean and are immediately sent hurtling to the low atmospheric pressures of the heated land surfaces of the Southern states. Ferrel's Law that all winds tend to turn to the right in the Northern Hemisphere is negligible in the hurricane's movements as it rushes down a steep pressure gradient to the heated land area. Florida is the nearest large land area to the breeding grounds; consequently the hurricanes bend their course toward the peninsula. Momentum carries them across into the Gulf of Mexico. From here they may head northward into the other Gulf States or may turn back to Florida and pass out into the Atlantic, where they are caught in a mighty trap—the heated area over the 50-mile wide Gulf Stream. The constant 80° temperature of the Gulf Stream forms a long corridor of light air between two walls of heavier air. It is along this corridor that the hurricane travels northward and passes only within 80 miles of St. Simons. Since it passes St. Simons on its left, as the hurricane moves northward, St. Simons lies in the less dangerous semi-circle of the hurricane, and the winds, therefore, over Georgia's islands are much less vicious than at other places that might lie in the right semi-circle of the progressing air mass.

The record of St. Simons' worst hurricanes in the last 150 years shows only four of any consequence and they were very small as compared to those occurring at places north and south of here. Only one of these took much life;

about 100 negro slaves crossing Hampton River in open boats in September, 1804, were drowned. The next most notable one was 9:00 o'clock in the morning, October 2, 1898, when a large portion of St. Simons was flooded by a hurricane wind that heaped up the highest rise of water ever witnessed locally. It was about five feet above the marshes. However, again there was no surge or wall of water over the islands and mainland, but merely a rise from the wind-sustained tides in the inlets and marsh streams, which seemed to overflow and flood, without rush, the marsh side of the islands at the same time the unusually high tides were flooding the beaches. The waters receded in a very few hours, having done their chief damage to livestock caught on the marshes.

In the hurricane of 1944, the winds reached 65 miles per hour and came from the northeast, starting about 9:00 o'clock in the morning of October 19. Only slight damage resulted.

Northeasters are mostly the famous trade winds. They vary in velocity from a zephyr to 25 miles per hour; they are intermittently rainy in summer and winter, and mostly dry in spring and fall. They always cause abnormally high tides but have their greatest effects when they occur at spring tides, especially the spring tides in April and October.

Most of the northeasters have a rising barometric pressure. This is a positive evidence of their being trade winds. Should a northeaster have a falling "glass," as the old skippers called it, it is then due to the disturbance of a cyclone at sea and the northeaster itself is part of the peripheral and counter-clock whirls of the cyclone.

The southeast winds are given by some authorities as the prevailing winds. From the meteorologist's records it is admitted that they qualify as such; but from their small effect on tides and waves and their consequent effect on the islands, they are quite secondary to the northeasters. Both of these winds have constancy and velocity sufficient to keep ground fogs from accumulating very often over the islands. And, incidentally, the islands are comparatively free from advection fogs also, since the warmth of the Gulf Stream lying nearby causes the winds in winter to have a tendency to blow from the land toward the sea.

The northeasters derive their greater effect, on the tides and waves, over the southeasters because of the longer periods of uninterrupted blowing. The southeasters are daily winds, beginning around 12:00 o'clock noon and blowing steadily till 1:00 o'clock that night, at which time a west wind springs up and blows the waters back to sea, thus nullifying the effect of the southeasters.

Northeasters, however, blow for 24 hours a day and for several days at a time. Therefore, their effect on the tides is accumulative; the ebb tides are not allowed to fully recede but are held into shore and in the marsh streams. Each flood tide, therefore, grows larger and larger and more active erosively.

Northeasters have, in addition to their own force, a littoral current that normally flows southward. This coastwise current stems from the Gulf Stream. If one stirs the water in a bath tub by moving the hand several times in the water in the same direction and in the center, the soap suds will flow in the opposite direction at the edges of the water next to the tub. The Gulf Stream shuts off the tub from the rest of the ocean at Palm Beach and Hatteras and a compensating current is set up, flowing southward near the shore between these points and continuous except when interrupted by winds and tides at inlets, sounds, and rivers.

The tides in the concave south Atlantic coast are higher than at the immediate points above and below. They

SHOWING GULF STREAM AND LITTORAL CURRENT

have a normal range of 6 feet at neaps to 8 feet at springs, when they are not influenced by storm conditions. The highest rise is at Tybee and St. Simons, which are at the middle of the concavity. As was said previously, tides, like a pendulum, depend on a correlation of depth and distance of swing in at least a partly confined segment of

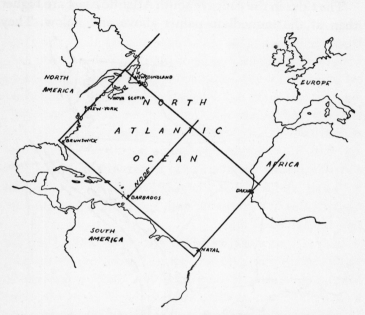

TIDAL BASIN OF THE ATLANTIC AFFECTING TIDES
FOR THE AMERICAN COAST LINE

the ocean. Georgia's islands form part of the end of such a marine basin. The complete end of the basin, of which the Georgia coast is a part, extends 1800 miles from Newfoundland to Florida. Its southwest side is formed by Florida, Cuba, Haiti and Dominican Republic, Puerto

Rico, the Leeward and Windward Islands, and the northeast shore of South America from Venezuela to Natal, Brazil, in all some 3600 miles.

The southeast line is the open sea from Natal to Liberia, Africa; and from there the fourth side extends to Newfoundland, the starting point.

From a point half the length of the box near the Barbados there runs a perpendicular which separates this basin in halves. This mid-line is called the node. The nodal line is the mid-point of the tidal swing or the lowest point of a pendulum's swing. The water neither rises nor falls at this line. Twice a day, or nearly so, the giant water pendulum cushions itself on our Atlantic seaboard, and twice a day it swings away leaving our beaches low and flat. But the tidal rise is not the same all along the American Coast. Its average at Brunswick and Savannah is 7½ feet, and 5 feet at Charleston and Jacksonville. The higher tides at Brunswick and Savannah are caused by the concave coast line.

Thus it is seen that winds, currents, and tides keep the waters surrounding the sea islands in continuous motion. Marine gradation is dependent on these water movements plus a source of materials which form the load. Marine gradation at the islands is dependent also on river gradation or the work of rivers that bring the material to the sea. The chief rock divisions of the Piedmont plateau and plain are metamorphic and igneous. The chief rocks of these divisions are granite, schists, and gneisses. The chief composing minerals of these rocks are quartz and feldspar. Quartz is the source of the beach sands; feldspar, when broken down chemically and mechanically,

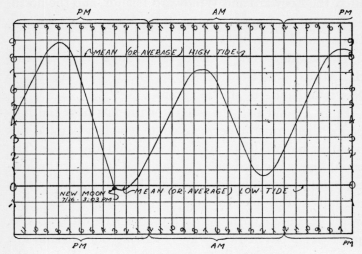

TYPICAL SPRING TIDE RECORDING

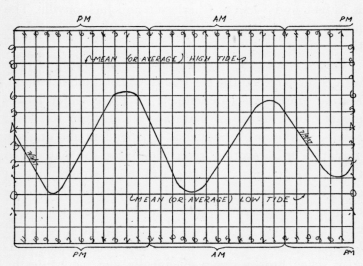

TYPICAL NEAP TIDE RECORDING

forms mud and silts, as seen in the marshes. Sand and silt are rushed from the land surfaces of Georgia by streams that never cease and that are nearly always heavily loaded. The load capacity of a stream varies directly as its velocity from the second to the sixth power. To illustrate: If a stream is carrying quartz grains of one millimeter in diameter when it flows at 3 feet per hour it would carry grains 4 to 64 times larger if the flow should suddenly be doubled. The reverse is just as true. If its velocity is cut in half the flow could only carry particles from $\frac{1}{4}$ to $\frac{1}{64}$ as large. This is very important in studying any form of gradation, which means in great part the picking up, moving, or depositing water borne materials.

The Savannah, Ogeechee, and Altamaha Rivers are bringing daily to our coastal waters hundreds of tons of sand and silt. When the rivers enter the ocean their velocities are lost and they unload. From here on the ocean waters, by means of the currents, tides, and waves, start a transportation system of their own. The carrying capacity of these sea agencies also depends on the velocity of the moving waters.

Waves are oscillatory in motion, that is, a particle of water swings back and forth while the wave travels on. If there is no current or wind or tide a boat does not travel with a wave, it only rides back and forth the width of the wave, and up and down the height of the wave, provided the width of the wave is less than the depth of the water at that point. If the depth is less than the width of the waves, as is the case on Georgia's islands, then the large oscillatory waves are transformed into translatory waves. A translatory wave may be described as an oscillatory wave that has stubbed its toe on the bottom and is now falling forward. A particle in a translatory wave has a forward or landward motion with each wave. This is made use of by the surf board riders at Waikiki, Hawaii, and to some extent at St. Simons and Sea Island.

Georgia's rivers to the Atlantic flow consistently down the southeastern slope of the coastal plain and enter the ocean in this direction or rather the tides of the ocean

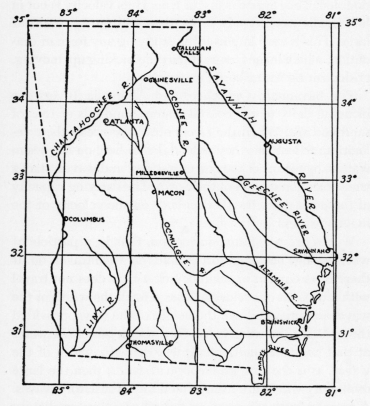

GEORGIA RIVERS FLOWING INTO ATLANTIC OCEAN

meet them up their channels from this direction. As the currents from the flood tides meet the currents of the rivers head-on the heavier particles of the river loads are immediately precipitated from the loss of velocity. Rich delta soils are there deposited in the form of islands, adjoining fresh water marshes, and cultivatable fields. Examples are Butler Island, the Hofwyl, Altama and Hopeton Plantations, with their rice fields and rich farming soils near the mouth of the Altamaha River. However, when the rivers, temporarily dammed up by the flood tide, are released by the ebb tide they combine their flow with that of the outgoing tide to produce a strong current. The river and sea waters not only cease losing their loads but begin picking up new loads below their meeting point.

These loads are carried down to the sea and deposited from the shore line to many miles out. From here they begin a southward journey carried by the littoral current and translatory waves directed by northeasters. As they come to tidal inlets, whether large or small, their control is now shared by the tides. They are deposited as bars near the inlet entrances and as sand spits in some instances. The south end of Sea Island is such a spit and has been two hundred years in reaching its present length and size. Tybee was built from sands brought down by the Savannah River.

Once the bars are formed they have a shoreward direction of movement and a southward growth.

The courses of a grain of sand and a particle of silt brought to the sea by the Altamaha River are described. The sand has a diameter of 0.2 of a millimeter and the silt 0.001 of a millimeter. As mentioned, the materials brought by the river are surrendered to the ocean when the streams lose their velocity on entering the ocean. But the littoral current flowing south, as a compensatory movement to the Gulf Stream, picks up the sand and starts it southward. The movement is fairly slow unless a northeast wind should start blowing; in that case the particles of sand along with many others that now join it under the combined velocities of current and wind, increase the speed of their movement southward until they come to an opening between two islands along whose vicinity they travel. At this point a third current joins in to further complicate the movement; it is the tides that flow in and out of such inlets. Tidal movement like the littoral current reaches to the bottom of the ocean. If the current, the wind, and the tide should have the same or similar directions the load is greatly increased and carried much farther. But if, as happens most of the time, some or all of these conflict, then deposits are made in the form of bars or barrier reefs of sand. When a favorable resultant from the littoral current, translatory waves, and tides takes over, the bars are moved closer and closer to the shore line and the closer they approach the higher they get. The tides and translatory waves wash these former bars a little at a time up on the beaches. Little St. Simons, Sea Island, East Beach, and Little Cumberland are huge sand reefs rolled and blown up against the original islands of which they now form integral parts.

Ebb tides leave the beaches bare and exposed to the drying effects of the sun and the winds. The Altamaha grain of sand washed up on St. Simons beach dries out and is now ready to be taken over by another transporting agent, the wind. Again the northeast wind is the prevailing one to move the sand. Any growth—grass, bushes or trees—starts dunes. The dunes themselves are also subject to a forward movement from the northeast winds. They will often engulf a copse of dense woods, move on over or through them at a rate of 5 feet a year. They will increase an island's general level above the sea by being spread out or left in long parallel ridges. In some instances they move out on the marshes and build them into land that is above the tides, as was mentioned regarding Sea Island and East Beach.

Silt brought down by the Altamaha has a disposal quite different from that of the sand. Some was deposited as delta material as mentioned. According to the transportation formula the finer silt particles should stay in suspension much longer than the sand and should be almost permanently suspended in the constantly moving ocean waters. In fact, if this formula alone were involved our oceans would be so muddy all over the world that much of their life, plant and animal, would be threatened, their beautiful aquamarine colors non-existent and there would be no marshes.

Since silt has a diameter less than .001 of a millimeter it grades into a colloidal solution. These particles all have the same electric charge and are so active in repelling each other they have great difficulty in settling in fresh water. Sea water, in contrast, is seldom muddy due to the fact that, being ionized from the electrolytes it holds in solution, the electric charges of the suspended silt particles are affected and flocculation can now form such large aggregates they rapidly settle. This explains why rivers have such dirty mouths where they empty into the oceans. Since the tides meet the rivers some distance up their channels the precipitated mud is available to the action of the marsh streams which transport it into the huge settling basins.

CONCLUSIONS

The islands are being constantly modified. There is no loss but a gain of growth from this modification. The sea level is rising faster than their growth. If no change occurs in the present rise of the sea level they will be submerged in one thousand years. There will be another and quite similar chain born as these pass out.

ADDENDA

GEORGIA'S GEOLOGIC TIME TABLE

ERA	PERIOD	EVENTS
CENOZOIC **50,000,000** **YEARS**	Recent Pleistocene Pliocene Miocene Oligocene Eocene	{ Islands and Continental glaciation Plains
	ROCKY MOUNTAINS	
MESOZOIC **100,000,000** **YEARS**	Cretaceous Jurassic Triassic	Coastal plains Basaltic Dykes
	APPALACHIAN MOUNTAINS	
PALEOZOIC **350,000,000** **YEARS**	Permian Pennsylvanian Mississippian Devonian Silurian Ordivician Cambrian Pre-Cambrian	Stone Mountain Mountain and Valley Regions Appalachia

ANALYSIS OF ARTESIAN WELL WATER

Chemical analysis of artesian well on Jekyll Island by H. C. White, State Chemist.

Solid Contents Dissolved	Grains per Gallon
Lime	8.08
Sulphate of Soda	3.86
Table Salt	1.46
Potassium Chloride	0.09
Sulphate of Lime	1.32
Epsom Salts	0.61
Quartz	0.07
Organic matter	1.26
Total solids per gallon	16.75 grains

ANALYSIS OF MARSH MUD

Analysis of marsh mud from St. Simons Island as made by Dr. Edgar Evarhart, State Chemist.

Moisture	4.62
Organic	9.94
Table Salt	4.83
Potash	1.13
Magnesium	1.28
Lime	0.40
Aluminum Oxide	13.67
Iron Oxide	4.86
Titanium Oxide	1.01
Sulphur Oxide	.24
Phosphorus Oxide	.22
Quartz	57.95
Total	100.15%

ANALYSIS OF OCEAN WATER

One hundred pounds of sea water contain 3½ pounds of mineral matter in solution. This matter is composed as follows:

Table Salt	77.76%
Magnesium Chloride	10.88%
Epsom Salts	4.74%
Calcium Sulphate	3.60%
Potassium Sulphate	2.47%
Lime	0.34%
Total	99.49%

The remaining 0.51% is composed of many other minerals present in very small quantities.

HOURLY WIND RECORDS

Hourly winds from records at McKinnon Air Port, St. Simons Island, showing typical daily change from prevailing SE to West at night.

August 19, 1939	Direction	Miles Per Hour	August 20, 1939	Direction	Miles Per Hour
AM 0.30	SE	11	AM 0.30	SW	9
1.30	SE	13	1.30	SW	5
2.30	SE	13	2.30	SW	7
3.30	SE	9	3.30	W	7
4.30	SW	11	4.30	W	5
5.30	SW	11	5.30	SW	7
6.30	SW	13	6.30	W	7
7.30	W	9	7.30	W	7
8.30	W	11	8.30	W	10
9.30	W	9	9.30	W	9
10.30	W	9	10.30	SW	9
11.30	W	13	11.30	SW	10
PM 12.30	W	14	PM 12.30	SW	10

August 19, 1939	Direction	Miles Per Hour	August 20, 1939	Direction	Miles Per Hour
1.30	W	14	1.30	W	9
2.30	SE	9	2.30	W	10
3.30	SE	16	3.30	SE	11
4.30	SE	14	4.30	SE	9
5.30	S	17	5.30	SE	13
6.30	S	11	6.30	SE	15
7.30	SW	14	7.30	SE	13
8.30	SW	9	8.30	SE	15
9.30	S	5	9.30	SE	17
10.30	SW	8	10.30	S	15
11.30	SW	7	11.30	W	15

Typical NE winds from St. Simons Island Coast Guard Station, comparing their steady blow with the intermittent winds of the day before.

February 11, 1946	Direction	Miles Per Hour	February 12, 1946	Direction	Miles Per Hour
AM 4.00	W	7	AM 4.00	NE	7
8.00	NW	12	8.00	NE	12
12.00	SE	7	12.00	NE	12
PM 4.00	E	5	PM 4.00	NE	7
8.00	SE	5	8.00	NE	7
12.00	NE	5	12.00	NE	5

LOG OF WELL DRILLED IN OIL EXPLORATION

Located 40 miles northeast of Brunswick, Georgia

DEPTH	DESCRIPTION
0– 40 feet	Sand and clay
40– 108	Sandy shale
108– 170	Sand, green shale and boulders

DEPTH	DESCRIPTION
170– 315	Sand and hard streaks
315– 515	Shale and streaks of sand and lime rock
515– 770	Lime and shells
770– 910	Lime
910– 965	Hard lime
965–1010	Hard broken lime
1010–1023	Brown hard limestone
1015–1052	Lime
1052–1145	Hard sand
1145–1195	Hard lime
1195–1265	Hard sand
1265–1380	Gray sandy lime
1380–1465	White lime
1465–1510	Hard sand and flint
1510–1515	Flint
1515–1578	Flint
1578–1594	Sandy lime
1594–1655	Sand lime
1655–1664	Hard lime
1664–1684	Hard lime
1684–1753	Hard lime
1753–1860	White lime and shell
1860–1863	Hard flint?
1863–1878	Hard lime
1878–1955	Lime
1955–2058	Sandy shale
2058–2178	Sandy shale and lime
2178–2227	Shale and lime
2227–2240	Sandy shale
2240–2341	Gray sandy lime
2341–2393	White lime and sand
2393–2510	Sandy shale

DEPTH	DESCRIPTION
2510–2720	Sandy shale
2720–2900	Sandy shale
2900–2990	Shale
2990–3020	Brown lime and shell
3020–3057	Shale
3057–3165	Sandy, shale
3165–3186	Sandy shale
3186–3273	Sandy, shale
3273–3314	Sandy, shale
3328–3410	Hard, sandy, shale
3410–3452	Shale
3452–3475	Soft sandy shale
3475–3495	Hard shale
3495–3513	Sandy shale
3513–3575	?
3575–3675	Shale
3675–3891	Sandy shale
3891–3903	Hard sand and lime
3903–4090	Sandy shale and lime
4090–4175	Shale, lime
4175–4206	Hard shale
4206–4211	Sandy shale
4211–4241	Sand and shale
4241–4311	Hard dark, shale
4311–4345	Hard dark shale
4345–4355	Granite arkose at top—hard granite at base (former peneplain or Appalachia)

4355 . . . . . . Total Depth

INDEX

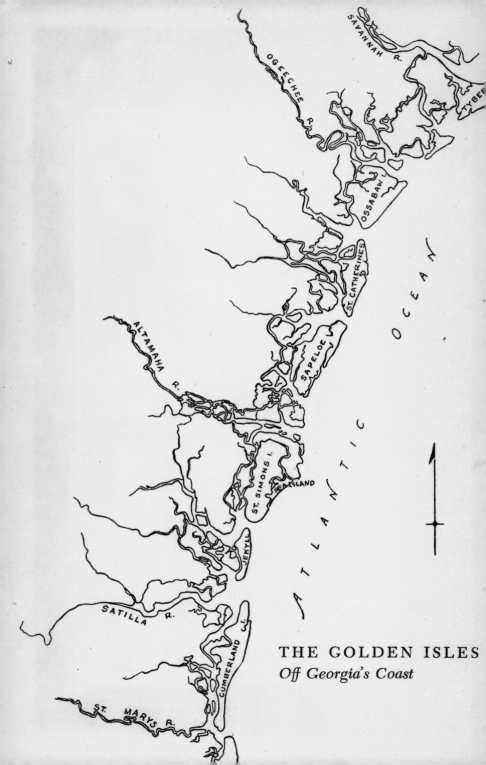

THE GOLDEN ISLES
Off Georgia's Coast